The Magic Employment Agency

Taylor Sapp

Alphabet Publishing

Contents

Before You Read

1. What are some jobs you would like to have?

2. What are some jobs you would never want to have?

3. What kind of magical or mythical creature would you want to be?

4. How would your daily life be different if you had magical powers? How would use your powers in your normal life?

5. Do you agree with the saying "Find a job you love and you'll never have to work a day in your life?" Why or why not?

The Magic Employment Agency

One of the main challenges of being an agent at the Magic Employment Agency is dealing with people who don't fit well into society. But the biggest challenge is what I love the most: finding a place for all people to con-
tribute.

And I mean everyone!

For example, there was Igor, the lab assistant to a mad scientist. I had a difficult time under-standing him. He could barely speak because his master had used him to test all sorts of po-tions and machines. Igor had been electrocuted, turned into animals, been made super strong and then super weak, become invisible, blind, deaf and more! And those are just examples of when the scientists' experiments went right! You don't want to know about the side effects of the experiments gone wrong!

The good news is that Igor was perfect for a very important job: safety inspector! Companies are always looking for someone to test the safety of their products and Igor was not afraid of getting hurt. Again.

Another time I was faced with a narcoleptic woman with bruises on her face. When she was a teenager, a fairy had cursed her so she slept for years and years. Even though a prince had kissed her and set her free, she still fell asleep unexpectedly sometimes. She couldn't really rule the kingdom like that. A desk job wouldn't work. She kept falling asleep and banging her head! So what did I come up with? Mattress tester!

My biggest challenge before today seemed an impossible challenge at the time: a man who had been turned to stone by Medusa. You know Medusa, right? Greek, snakes in her hair, turns everyone she looks at to stone? This guy tried to cut off her head and she looked at him. In an instant, he was a statue. Still alive, but a statue!

What do you do with a living statue? It turns out he's an excellent security camera watcher. He can still see and he can make a little bit of noise if he tries hard. But he never gets tired or needs a break or food!

I thought those would be my biggest challenges until today. For some reason, there were always big surprises on Tuesdays! And today there were three of them!

• • • ● •• ● • • ••

First, bright and early, a young woman came in carrying a small Chihuahua in her purse, just the head sticking out.

"You're Margarita Sobakina?"

She nodded then asked "Are you hungry?"

I was trying to figure out why she would say that to me. Then I realized she was looking at the dog. Even stranger, the dog was looking back at her and making a series of noises, as if responding.

"You know, we don't really allow..." I started to say, but Margarita interrupted me.

"Lily here is my Emotional Support Animal. I don't go anywhere without her."

"Is there a reason why you need an Emotional Support Animal?"

"Actually, ok fine. Lily is actually my mentor. She gives me advice during job interviews."

I needed a minute to process that. I'm used to getting unusual characters, but usually special characteristics are on the application form. Plus, bringing a helper could be breaking a rule. I'd think about that later.

For now, I decided to start with the biggest issue.

"So, you can talk to your dog? And it can talk to you?"

She sighed. "That's right. Actually all dogs."

"And this dog is your mentor. Was your grandma put into a new body after she passed? We get that a lot."

"No, no. Nothing like that. It's a long story."

Lily started to make dog noises, barking and growling. Margarita added, "Lily doesn't want to get into it here."

"I guess that's ok, as long as curses aren't involved. So is it just dogs? Or can you understand other animals as well."

"I've only been around dogs, though I've thought I might be able to talk to maybe horses or something, if I spent more time with them."

"How about cats?"

She shook her head violently. "I'm not a cat person."

"It seems quite obvious to me you'd make a good veterinarian for doctors, if what you say is true."

"I tried that," Margarita said, "But I don't have the patience to sit in an office all day. I like to be active."

"Grrr, yip, yap-yap...yap," Lily added.

Margarita looked at me, widened her eyes, and shrugged her shoulders. "See what I mean?"

"Straight from the dog's mouth," I said.

Then it came to me!

"It seems there's a doggie day care center nearby in need of a fitness coach to help some of the dogs maintain a healthy weight. I think you'd be able to provide the proper motivation."

Of course, with her communication skills, she would prove highly successful at this job.

I thought I'd gotten through my biggest challenge of the day early, but my day was only beginning.

· · · ● · ● · · ·

I had my next challenge right after lunch. He was an old man with a long white beard dressed in a large green robe and a pointy hat. He carried a magic wand in his right hand.

He spoke in a loud voice, "Good evening, young sir. May the fires of life be with you!"

I thanked him for the mysterious compliment as he sat down.

"Greendorf," he introduced himself, a single name. Before I could ask, I noticed he'd written it as both his first and last.

As I read his application, I saw he was making a small ball of fire in his hand.

"Sir, if you please..."

He nodded. "Sorry young man, just a nervous reaction."

"So, Mr. Dorf..."

"Greendorf," he corrected me.

"Your application says your past job was 'Protector of the Five Worlds'. I don't know what that means."

He laughed in a superior way. "There are five worlds in human life: the physical, emotional, practical, intellectual, and spiritual, all governed by earth, air, fire, and water. For centuries, I have protected these realms from any danger for the good of humanity."

I nodded. "And who was your employer? You list 'The Heavens'. Do you mean you were working for a church?"

Greendorf spoke at length about The Heavens and the Dark Ones and a force. I couldn't follow. I just stared at him. He saw my look then sat back and grumbled, "I suppose your idea of God is as close as you can get to understanding"

I continued looking at his application. "For skills, you've listed 'control of the elements, including space and time'."

"These are standard for any master wizard."

I nodded, because my mind was blank. I couldn't even understand what kind of wizard this guy was or what he could do. In order to stall, I stood up with my empty coffee mug. "If you'll excuse me, I'm just going to get another cup of coffee."

As I spoke, Greendorf waved his wand. Suddenly my cup was full of hot coffee again!

I sat back down and took a drink!

"Brazilian dark roast! You'd have great potential as a server at a coffee shop!"

Greendorf shuddered. "Heavens no! Coffee is a foul-tasting drink that turns humans into addicts. I promised to do no harm when I received my wizard hat and staff."

I made a note on his application, 'No coffee shops', a bit depressed that he'd shot down the suggestion so quickly.

I thought for a minute. "I'm trying to think. I assume you could create fire or summon a dragon..." Greendorf sighed and looked at with a bored face as if to say, "Of course."

"Now those are things we usually want to avoid in the workplace, so I think an office job is probably out."

And then it occurred to me.

I'd just finished lunch when Greendorf walked in and I still had my takeout bag from the seafood restaurant next door under my desk. I pulled out the empty cup of clam chowder from the bag.

"Can you do the same again with this?"

Greendorf smiled thinly and with a wave of his hand, I had another full cup of clam chowder!

"I've got it, Mr. Greendorf. There's a soup kitchen nearby looking for a full-time head chef. They don't pay much, but it's a government program so it has nice benefits."

Greendorf listened while playing with his beard.

"This place helps people in need? The innocent victims of an evil system?"

"The homeless, primarily, so yes, I suppose that's true."

"Then it would be my honor to accept such a responsibility. In fact, it is part of my wizard duty to do no harm, and to help all who need it! I have a really bad toothache, so I would hope dental care would be included?"

I smiled, certain the right match had been made. "You're in luck. Another of the positives of a government job!"

After that, from what I heard, Greendorf was a great hit, able to use magic to make an infinite amounts of delicious and healthy meals at the Pineview Community Soup Kitchen. Plus pizza Friday! And although he accidentally started a kitchen fire or two, luckily he also had the ability to put the fires out!

• • • ● • ● • • •

My day ended with my biggest challenge. A small creature with tiny wings covered in purple feathers flew into my office, application in mouth, laid it on my desk and perched on the chair. It was the size of a house cat, but its body looked a bit like a turkey and its face was more like an alligator, with a big snout and toothy jaws.

"Hi there. What's your name?"

"Chickoo!" I noticed that was also written as the first and last names. I shook my head again. What a day.

I took a look at the application, realizing I had more than a few small differences to deal with.

"So you haven't written a gender, and I'm also not clear about your species. You've written 'Chicken/Dragon'. Does that mean you're half-chicken and half-dragon?"

"Chickoo!" it said in a tone that sounded like yes.

"OK. You've listed two previous professions: fighting monsters and entertaining at birthday parties. We always need more cute unusual characters for children's birthday parties!

"Chickoo..." But this time it was said with sadness. I understood he had suffered trauma at a birthday party, not worth getting into.

"Any other skills?" I asked.

Chickoo looked at me, then started to shake. I was a bit afraid it would blow up or breathe fire, so I started to duck under my desk. Then the glow started. After a few seconds I decided it was safe to peek over the top of my desk. Chickoo was glowing with a very bright yellow light.

The strong light gave me some options to work with. I searched my database and quickly found the perfect match!

"Are you okay with being alone? I found a good job, also with benefits, but you could get lonely..."

"Chickoo," it said, with a confident tone

I found Chickoo a job at a lighthouse! It was a great success. Chickoo's flashing body was visible for miles and miles and it saved thousands of dollars in electric bills! Chickoo ended up transferring to the Bermuda Triangle where he was able to prevent any ships or planes from getting lost!

So overall it was a busy Tuesday, but there wasn't a challenge I couldn't handle. We'll see what next Tuesday brings at The Magic Employment Agency.

Glossary

clam chowder: a thick creamy soup with clams in it

compliment: nice words to a person

cursed: having harmful magic put on you

Emotional Support Animal: An animal that helps people who have emotional or psychological problems

fairy: a magical creature that can help or hurt people

glow: a bright light

grumbled: speak in a low unclear voice, often while complaining

infinite: unending

mentor: a successful person who helps you in your career

narcoleptic: a person suffering from a condition that makes you fall asleep unexpectedly

perched: sitting in a bird-like way

potions: a liquid that has magical effects on the person who drinks it

robe: a long piece of clothing that covers most of your body, often worn at ceremonies

shrugged: moved shoulders up and down to show lack of knowledge

shuddered: shook quickly out of fear or cold

snout: the part on some animals that contains the nose and mouth sticking out of the face

summon: cause to appear

takeout: for food that is taken out of a restaurant and eaten at home or work

After You Read

1. What is it about this employment agency that makes finding jobs more difficult?

2. Which character do you think had the oddest skill set?

3. Which job did the narrator find for each character?

4. What other jobs could you think of for the characters?

5. What job do you think your personality is suited for?

6. Do you have any special skills that you think could work in an unusual job?

Writing

Imagine another client that needs a job.

- What is unusual about them?

- What jobs have they had before?

- What job will the narrator find for them?

- How do you think the narrator got their job?

More Readers

AlphabetPublish.com/Book-Category/
Graded-Reader